A BRIDGE WITH A HOUSE...
OREGON'S COVERED BRIDGES

STEVEN E. HUNNICUTT

BookVenture Publishing LLC
1000 Country Lane Ste 300
Ishpeming MI 49849
www.bookventure.com
Hotline: 1(877) 276-9751
Fax: 1(877) 864-1686

Ordering Information:
Quantity sales. Special discounts are available on quantity purchases by corporations, associations, and others. For details, contact the publisher at the address above.

Printed in the United States of America.

Library of Congress Control Number		2017961778
ISBN-13:	Softcover	978-1-64166-276-5
	Hardcover	978-1-64166-277-2
	Pdf	978-1-64166-278-9
	ePub	978-1-64166-279-6
	Kindle	978-1-64166-280-2

My name is Steven Hunnicutt, who does "projects". Best way to define, is anything that brings out the creative side of me.

Oregon Covered Bridges is one such project.

It started in October 2004 visiting the covered bridges of Cottage Grove, Oregon and ended with a visit to Cedar Crossing Covered Bridge in Portland, Oregon, February 2007.

The project evolved into this book, pictures of the covered bridges, overview on history and facts of covered bridges.

It is also a chance to show off Oregon, to those who live here and those who don't.

Covered Bridges tells the history of Oregon.

It is a just a "Coffee Table" book, enjoy.

A Bridge with a House
A Covered Bridge

A Bridge with a House

Compiled

And

Photographed

By

Steven E Hunnicutt

Oregon's Covered Bridges

Dedicated to;

Julie, my wife, who endured the journey

In Memory of

My Mom

Anna Johanna Yntema Hunnicutt

1920-2011

My Father-in-Law

Eugene "Jeep" Vanicek

1927-2012

To A Very Special Friend

Who contributed suggestions and encouragement.

Shirley Baldwin

A Bridge with a House

Who would want to live on a bridge?

Why would you need a house for a bridge?

Here in Oregon we have bridges with houses.

A bridge with a house for cattle,

A bridge with a house for trains,

A bridge with a house for people, horses, wagons,

A bridge with a house for kissing.

A bridge with a house that dotted the country side, four-hundred plus,

Fifty-One are all that are left.

A bridge with a house that tells a part of our history,

Fifty-One are all that are left.

A bridge with a house mostly found on the "blue highway",

Overlooked, forgotten, driven by.

A bridge with a house that would last eighty years and longer,

Without the house, nine years at best.

A bridge with a house built by individuals, built by companies,

Built by the state.

A bridge with a house that began to dot the country side when Oregon became a state.

A bridge with a house for a land that in later years became known as

"The Pacific Northwet"

A bridge with a house, each unique, each with a story, the Fifty-One left,

Their story is of survival,

Their story is of individuals preserving them,

Their story is of a state that realizes that this is a part of our history,

The "Need" and the "Want" to saved them is just that,

It is a part of us, it is a part of "Our Family", we "Need" and "Want"

To take care of our "Family"

A Covered Bridge

Covered bridges can be dated back two thousand years, to a time they were being built in China and even earlier in ancient Babylon (780 B.C.)

Contents

First covered bridge built in America was built in 1804 by Theodore Burr of Connecticut. This bridge spanned the Hudson River in New York and was called the Waterford Bridge, lasting 105 years.

First covered bridge built in Oregon was in 1851, Oregon City. The second 1852, also in Oregon City. Both bridges were eventually swept away by flood waters in January 1853.

Listing of Covered Bridges

By

County

Benton

Irish Bend

Harris

Hayden

Coos

Sandy

Douglas

Cavitt Creek

Horse Creek

Neal Lane

Pass Creek

Rochester

Jackson

Antelope Creek

Lost Creek

McKee

Wimer

Josephine

Grave Creek

Lane

Wildcat

Earnest

Pengra Creek

Lake Creek

Coyote

Parvin Creek

Goodpasture

Belknap

Office Creek

Lowell Creek

Deadwood

Wendling Creek

Unity Creek

Cottage Grove

"Covered Bridge Capital of Oregon"

Centennial

Stewart Creek

Mosby Creek

Currin

Dorena

Chambers 1925

Chambers 2011

Lincoln

Chitwood

Drift Creek

Five Rivers

Yachats

Linn

Crawfordsville

Gilkey

Hannah

Hoffman

Larwood

Shimanek

Short

Weddle

Marion

Gallon House

Stayton-Jordan

Polk

Ritner

Fourtner

Listing of
"Not All Bridges that are Covered are Covered Bridges"

Lane

Cannon Covered (Street) Bridge

Linn

Dahlenburg

Whittemore

Douglas

Canyon Creek

Milo Academy

Deschutes

Rock O' The Range

Multnomah

Cedar Crossing

A Bridge with a House

A bridge with a roof and walls that protect it against the weather.

A bridge whose roadway is protected by a roof and sides.

A timber structure supporting a deck surface that carries loads over an obstruction (e.g., a river).

Components are protected from the elements by various covering: walls, roofs, and decks.

A Covered Bridge

They represent more than a simple conveyance; they are a part of the character of the communities in which they serve.

They are one of those quality of life resources which can not be measured in dollars and cents.

HAYDEN BRIDGE
1918

Benton County

Irish Bend Covered Bridge

Built – 1954

Truss – Howe

Span – 60 Feet

Stream – Oak Creek

It is thought to have been constructed over the Long Tom River and then floated down stream to provide access across the Willamette Slough on Irish Bend Road.

In 1975, realignment of the road, the bridge was not used, it was dismantled in 1988.

The Irish Bend Advisory Committee and Benton County reconstructed the bridge on Oregon State University, the completion was 1989, cost $60,000 along with donated timbers and foundation.

Harris Covered Bridge
(Mary's River Covered Bridge)

Built – 1936 *1929

Truss – Howe

Span – 75 Feet

Stream – Mary's River

As to when it was built, is in question, Benton County records show 1936, the locals claim it may have been built in 1929.

H.W. Fiedler built the bridge to replace a bridge at the same site.

Harris has been a community since 1890.

Hayden Covered Bridge
(Alsea River Covered Bridge)

Built – 1918

Truss – Howe

Span – 90 Feet

Stream – Alsea River

The name is derived from the name of an Indian tribe living at the mouth of the river, originally pronounced in three syllables.

It is the only covered bridge still standing on a primary state highway.

Oregon – 6th largest collection in the U.S.

Lane Country – Most west of the Mississippi

Cottage Grove – Known as "The Covered Bridge Capital of Oregon"

Scio – Known as "The Covered Bridge Capital of the West"

The Oregon Trail ended when you crossed a Covered Bridge.

1st Covered Bridge – Oregon City, 1851, eight years before Oregon became a state.

Coos County

Sandy Creek Covered Bridge

(Remote Covered Bridge)

Built – 1921

Truss – Howe

Span – 60 Feet

Stream – Sandy Creek

The only remaining covered span in Coos County, carried traffic on Highway 42 until it was bypassed in 1949.

In 1982 a new roof, replacing boards and structural pieces, clearing brush and applying a coat of white paint.

In 1984 the bridge was dedicated as a Coos County Park.

Remote received its name, it is believed, due to it's geographic isolation.

Built with Douglas Fir, abundant, suited for bridge construction.

Built to withstand heavy rains and salty sea air.

Suited for woodland country.

Provided access to timber and land.

Douglas County

Cavitt Creek Covered Bridge
(Little River Covered Bridge)

Built – 1943

Truss – Howe

Span – 70 Feet

Stream – Little River

Built by Floyd Frear, noted Douglas County builder.

Robert Cavitt was a settler in the early 1880's who settled on a tributary of the Little River.

The bridge has a metal roof and floor with longitudinal running planks. The structure sits on concrete piers.

Horse Creek Covered Bridge
(Myrtle Creek Covered Bridge)

Built – 1930 *1990

Truss – Howe

Length – 105 Feet

Stream – Myrtle Creek

Originally spanned Horse Creek in the vicinity of McKenzie Bridge in Lane County.

In 1968 bypassed by a concrete span, removed December 1987.

The timbers were given to the city of Cottage Grove for salvage, which were then used to construct a small-scale covered bridge in their park.

(Centennial Covered Bridge)

1990 the remaining lumber was donated to the City of Myrtle Creek. The structure now spans the stream of Myrtle Creek and provides access from a parking area into the Mill Site Park.

33

Neal Lane Covered Bridge

(South Myrtle Creek Covered Bridge)

Built – 1939 *1929

Truss – Kingpost

Span – 42 Feet

Stream – South Myrtle Creek

Cost - $1000.00

One of the shortest covered bridges in Oregon.

The only roofed span in Oregon using a Kingpost truss design.

A local resident claims to have been a workman on the bridge in 1939, construction date shows 1929.

Pass Creek Covered Bridge

Built – 1925 *1906 1989

Truss – Howe

Span – 61 Feet

Stream – Pass Creek

Members of the Umpqua Historic Preservation Society attest the span was constructed in 1906.

The original bridge was built in the 1870's and an 1895-era photograph shows the wagon bridge and adjacent railroad bridge both being covered.

It is probable the covered wagon bridge was either rebuilt or replaced in 1925.

Calapooya Creek Covered Bridge
(Rochester Covered Bridge)

Built – 1933

Truss – Howe

Span – 80 Feet

Stream – Calapooya Creek

Unique among Oregon Covered bridges, windows having graceful curved tops.

Builder Floyd Frear, combined both beauty and strength.

When another nearby covered bridge was torched in the 1950's to make way for a new concrete bridge, local residents sat through the night with guns and rifles to safeguard the covered bridge which was dilapidated at the time, it was saved.

Was remodeled in 1969 by county crews.

Similar to barns, easier to transport cattle, livestock, would not be starled.

Protect the trusses from the weather.

Insulation for the timber, more uniform temperature conditions.

Strengthened the entire struction.

Jackson
County

Antelope Creek Covered Bridge
(Little Butte Creek Covered Bridge)

Built – 1922 *1987

Truss – Queensport (modified by Kingsport bracing)

Span – 58 Feet

Stream – Little Butte Creek

The only Oregon covered bridge equipped with a fire-protection sprinkler system.

In 1987 years after it had been closed to traffic, the townsfolk of Eagle Point loaded it onto a make shift trailer and rebuilt it at its new site.

Lost Creek Covered Bridge

Built – 1919 *1881

Truss – Queensport

Span – 39 Feet

Stream – Lost Creek

It is the shortest of all Oregon Covered Bridges.

Shirley Stone, daughter of John Walch, claims the Lost Creek Bridge to have been built as early as 1878-1881.

Johnny Miller, the builder of Lost Creek Bridge, reroofed the bridge in the early 1880's, it is recorded. The date could be maintenance records.

This would make it Oregon's oldest standing covered bridge, beating out Drift Creek Covered Bridge (1914).

McKee Covered Bridge

(Applegate River Covered Bridge)

Built – 1917

Truss – Howe

Span – 122 Feet

Stream – Applegate River

8 miles from the California border.

1917-1956, mining and logging traffic.

Built by contractor Jason Hartman and his son Wesly
on land donated by Aldelbert "Deb" McKee.

Wimer Covered Bridge
(Evans Creek Covered Bridge)

Built – 1927 *1892 *2008

Truss – Queensport

Length – 85 Feet

Stream – Evans Creek

Community members insist that the original bridge was built in 1892, the Hartman brothers of Jacksonville replaced the Wimer Bridge in 1927.

It collapsed July 6, 2003 and was rebuilt 2008.

Truss Type

Kingpost

Simplistic and easy design, single pieces of wood for the beams.

Constraint on size of bridge, trees only grow so tall.

Josephine County

Grave Creek Covered Bridge

Built – 1920

Truss – Howe

Span – 105 Feet

Stream – Grave Creek

The last covered bridge on the north/south pacific highway system.

Cost - $21,128.00

53

Truss Type

Queenpost

Adding another vertical beam, the truss could be made much longer, but like the Kingpost, only a certain length could be attained.

Lane County

Wildcat Covered Bridge

(Austa Covered Bridge)

Built – 1925

Truss – Howe

Span – 75 Feet

Stream – Wildcat Creek

Stagecoach Road was the original road to the coast until the 1930's when the Linslaw Tunnel and Mapleton Bridge were built.

Earnest Covered Bridge

(Adams Bridge)

Built – 1938

Truss – Howe

Span – 75 Feet

Stream – McKenzie River

The original bridge was built in 1903 by A.C. Striker, called Adams Bridge.

In 1938 Lane County replaced it for a cost of $2,449 and was renamed after a long time local resident.

It was in the movie "Shenandoah", starring James Stewart and Doug McClure, filmed in the mid 60's.

The bridge was altered to reflect Civil War architecture and then restored back to the original condition.

Pengra Creek Covered Bridge

Built – 1938

Truss – Howe

Span – 120 Feet

Stream – Fall Creek

Contains two of the longest timbers ever cut for a bridge in Oregon.

The lower cords 16"x18"x126'

The bridge was named for B.J. Pengra, a pioneer who eventually became General Surveyor of Oregon in 1862.

Lake Creek Covered Bridge
(Nelson Mountain Covered Bridge)

Built – 1928

Truss – Howe

Span – 105 Feet

Stream – Lake Creek

Nelson Mountain is the name of the road the covered bridge is on.

Many covered bridges, the upper and lower chords are on a piece of old-growth timber.

Coyote Covered Bridge

(Battle Creek Covered Bridge)

(Swing Log Covered Bridge)

Built – 1922

Truss – Howe

Span – 60 Feet

Stream – Coyote Creek

Referred to as Battle Creek Covered Bridge because it is located on Battle Creek Road.

Swing Log Covered Bridge was a name used many years ago.

Parvin Creek Covered Bridge

Built – 1921

Truss – Howe

Span – 75 Feet

Stream – Lost Creek

Cost - $3,600

Bypassed in the mid 1970's, reopened in 1986 and attending the opening ceremony were the Granddaughters of James and Salina Parvin, settlers who homesteaded in the area during the 1850's.

Goodpasture Covered Bridge
(McKenzie River Covered Bridge)

Built – 1938

Truss – Howe

Span – 165 Feet

Stream – McKenzie River

The most photographed covered bridge in Oregon.

Cost - $13,154

The longest covered bridge still in daily use.

The name is from the Goodpasture family who settled near the town of Vida and gave their name to the bridge.

Belknap Covered Bridge

Built – 1966

Truss – Howe

Span – 120 Feet

Stream – McKenzie River

A site in which a covered bridge has been in continous use since 1890.

The current bridge was designed by the Oregon Bridge Corporation, after the last one was destroyed in the Christmas Flood of 1964.

Louvered arch windows were added in 1975 to the south to provide interior illumination.

Office Creek Covered Bridge

Built – 1944

Truss – Howe

Span – 180 Feet

Stream – North Fork of the Middle Fork, Willamette River

At 180 feet it is the longest covered bridge in Oregon.

The bridge is one of only two covered bridges constructed with triple truss member used for log trucks.

A covered walkway on the side of the bridge, separate from the roadway, is another distinctive feature.

Truss Type
Howe

In 1840 Massachusetts builder William Howe solved the length problem, he introduced iron wooden truss design by substituting adjustable iron rods for the vertical members of the Long's Truss (Truss Type).

Long beams were no longer needed, to make the truss longer was to add more diagonal beams.

The Howe Truss utilized one of the greatest advantage of all over the other truss designs. This was the use of steel vertical supports, uses the strength of wood and steel to make a really study truss.

World Guide Numbers

State – Oregon is 37

County – Assigned Alphabetically

Bridge – Identifier, Location

(If bridge is no longer, the number is not reused or reassigned)

Letter at End – Denotes a bridge which does not use a true truss for support but is covered

Example -   37   20   35

Oregon Lane Earnest Bridge

Lowell Creek Covered Bridge

Built – 1945

Interpretive Center – 2006

Truss – Howe

Span – 165 Feet

Stream – Middle Fork of the Willamette River

Bypassed by a concrete bridge in 1981.

Interpretive Center

Dedication July 28, 2006

$1.2 million project of the Oregon Department of Transportation, Lane County, U.S. Forest Service and Western Federal Lands Highway Division, to showcase the Lowell Covered Bridge and the area's history.

Deadwood Covered Bridge

Built – 1932

Repaired – 1986

Truss – Howe

Span – 105 Feet

Stream – Deadwood Creek

Architectural Elements – flooring at a slant so that traffic rounding the corner onto the bridge would travel more safely.

Cost - $4,814

Wendling Creek Covered Bridge

Built – 1938

Truss – Howe

Span – 60 Feet

Stream – Mill Creek

Cost - $2,241

One of four built by Lane County in 1938.

(Earnest, Pengra, Goodpasture)

Unity Creek Covered Bridge

Built – 1936

Truss – Howe

Span – 90 Feet

Stream – Fall Creek

Cost - $4,400

A full length window on the east side
to give motorist a glimpse of oncoming traffic.

Due to its proximity to Pengra, Lowell, and Pavin
Covered Bridges, many bicycling tours include this on
their rural routes.

Oldest?

Drift Creek

1914

Lost Creek

1881

Research is still continuing as to which is the oldest.

Covered Bridge
Capital
Of
Oregon
Cottage Grove

Centennial Covered Bridge

Built – 1987

Truss – Howe

Span – 84 Feet

Stream – Coast Fork Willamette River

A 3/8 scale model of the Chambers Covered Bridge, constructed from dismantled Meadows and Brumbaugh Covered Bridge.

The bridge honors the 100th Birthday of Cottage Grove.

It is only 10 feet wide and 14 feet high and thus only handles foot and bicycle traffic.

Stewart Creek Covered Bridge

Built – 1930

Truss – Howe

Span – 60 Feet

Stream – Mosby Creek

"Mothballed" in 1987, a concrete bridge took its place.

From 1993 to 1995 with a grant from the Oregon Covered Bridge Program, $48,000, it was restored.

Mosby Creel Covered Bridge

Built – 1920

Truss – Howe

Span – 90 Feet

Stream – Mosby Creek

Lane County's oldest covered bridge.

Cost - $4,125

Named for David Mosby who settled in 1853 and staked claim to 1,600 acres east of the present day city of Cottage Grove.

It is still in service and receives regular maintenance by Lane County crews.

Currin Covered Bridge
(Row River Covered Bridge)

Built – 1925

Truss – Howe

Span – 105 Feet

Stream – Row River

Sometimes referred to as the Row River Bridge because of the stream it crosses.

The original bridge was built by Nels Roney in 1883 for $1,935. The bridge was replaced in 1925 and the county officials decided it could build the bridge cheaper than the lowest bid of $6,250, county employees constructed the bridge for $4,205.

It is the only Lane County covered bridge with white portals and red sides.

Dorena Covered Bridge
(Star Bridge)

Built – 1925

Truss – Howe

Span – 105 Feet

Stream – Row River

Built in conjunction with the completion of Dorena Dam.

Sometimes referred to as Star Bridge, large private estate today about 100 acreas.

The original town site was name for Dora Burnette and Rena Martin (Combining their first names), the town site is underwater at the bottom of the reservoir.

In 1974 it was bypassed by a concrete bridge, it is a part of a rest area overlooking Dorena Reservoir.

Chambers Covered Bridge

Built – 1925

Truss – Howe

Length – 78 Feet

Stream – Coast Fork of the Willamette River

It was the last covered railroad bridge in Oregon.

Operation 1925 – 1951

In private ownership until December 2006 when the City of Cottage Grove bought it.

February 2010 the bridge was dismantled due to leaning.

Chambers Covered Bridge

Built 2011

Truss – Howe

Length – 78 Feet

Stream – Coast Fork of the Willamette River

The replacement of the original.

Reconstruction began March 2011

December 3, 2011 a Dedication Ceremony was held.

Early February 2012 the covered bridge was completed with the installation of the roof.

Oregon Heyday of

Covered Bridges

1905 – 1925

450

2011

51

Lincoln County

Chitwood Covered Bridge

(Yaquina River Covered Bridge)

Built – 1926

Truss – Howe

Length – 96 Feet

Stream – Yaquina River

Logging in the area once boomed enough to support a community.

In the early 1900's Chitwood became an important rail stop for steam locomotives from Yaquina to Corvallis, as the town where the engines took on water and fuel as well as passengers and freight.

In 1982 the bridge was seriously damaged and needed to be repaired. In December 1983 work has been completed at the cost of $240,000.

Dedication ceremonies in January 1986 included a recitation of the history of the area and a parade of vintage cars.

Drift Creek Covered Bridge
(Bear Creek Covered Bridge)

Built – 1914 *2000

Truss – Howe

Span – 66 Feet

Stream – Bear Creek

Originally built south of Lincoln City, only 105 miles from the coast. The span once served traffic on a main north-south route along the coast.

The community surrounding the bridge site was known as Lutgens, and in 1917 was changed to Nice. In all, at least eight names changes occurred in this community prior to the closing of the post office in 1919.

Bypassed in the mid-1960's, unsafe in 1988, dismantled in 1997.

Timbers sold to Laura and Kerry Sweitz, who rebuilt the bridge on their property to have access across Bear Creek.

Five Rivers Covered Bridge

(Fisher School Covered Bridge)

Built – 1919 *1927

Truss – Howe

Length – 72 Feet

Stream – Five Rivers

Named because of the five streams of Alder Creek, Cougar Creek, Buck Creek, Crab Creek, and Cherry Creek, which make up the stream.

1919 Cost - $2,500

1927 renovation Cost - $1,800

The area around Five Rivers was the site of other covered bridges, including the 36 foot Buck Creek Bridge built in 1924. Two miles north of Fisher and the Cascade Creek Bridge. Only the Five Rivers or Fisher School bridge remains.

It is the close proximity of Fisher Elemnetary School that some refer to the bridge as the Fisher School Covered Bridge.

Yachats Covered Bridge

Built – 1938

(restored – 1989)

Truss – Queenpost

Span – 42 Feet

Stream – North Fork

One of the few remaining covered bridges with a Queenpost Truss.

A Bridge with a House

Remind us:

Of the Horse and Buggy Day.

Of a Slower Pace of Live.

Of a Town long since gone.

Of a Company who's time as past.

Of People who's skills lost for the ages.

Of Our New England influence.

Of Our Past.

A Covered Bridge

Linn
County

Crawsfordsville Covered Bridge

(Calapooia River Covered Bridge)

Built – 1932

Truss – Howe

Length – 105 Feet

Stream – Calapooia River

Named for Philemon Crawford who settled in the area and whose land the town was established in the 1870's.

In 1963 the bridge was bypassed and control of the bridge was relinquished to Linn County and now to Linn County parks and Recreation Department.

In 1987, $23,000 in materials and labor to renovate the bridge as a project of the Community Services Consortium, a federally funded program that trained and assisted in the job search for unemployed workers.

1996, $24,000 grant from Oregon Covered Bridge Program to replace

four floor beams, supporting rods, and paint for the bridge.

Gilkey Covered Bridge

Built – 1939 *1998

Truss – Howe

Length – 120 Feet

Stream – Thomas Creek

Named for Allen and William Gilkey.
Gilkey served as a shipping point for farm products.

Overloaded vehicles caused damaged to the bridge and in 1997 the bridge was closed while repairs were made and reopened in 1998.

Hannah Covered Bridge
(Thomas Creek Covered Bridge)

Built – 1936

Truss – Howe

Length – 105 Feet

Stream – Thomas Creek

Named for Joseph Hannah, arriving by wagon train and was granted a 151 acrea tract of land, bound by Thomas Creek and Bilyeu Creek.

Hannah built a sawmill which was powered by water from Bilyeu Creek.

Hoffman Covered Bridge

Built – 1936

Truss – Howe

Span – 90 Feet

Stream – Crabtree Creek

Named for Lee Hoffman, the man who built it.

Gothic style windows were used instead of the usual open Linn County truss design.

Larwood Covered Bridge

(Crabtree Creek Covered Bridge)

Built – 1939

Truss – Howe

Span – 105 Feet

Stream – Crabtree Creek)

Roaring River which empties into Crabtree Creek, is the only river to flow into a creek. This is an oddity in U.S. geography, it was featured in Ripley's Believe It or Not.

Named for William Larwood who settled on the banks of Crabtree Creek and Roaring River in 1888.

Shimanek Cover Bridge

(Thomas Creek Covered Bridge)

Built – 1966

Truss – Howe

Span – 130 Feet

Stream – Thomas Creek

Newest and longest covered bridge.

The first bridge at this location is believed to have been constructed in 1861, for a cost of $1,150.

1904 the bridge was rebuilt, it washed away in 1921. It was replaced and only lasted until 1927 when high water damaged it.

The fourth bridge was damaged during the Columbus Day storm of 1962, the bridge was finally destroyed.

1966 the current bridge was completed, the fifth to occupy this sight.

The 1891 bridge had a two-hole toilet built into the foundation.

Short Covered Bridge
(South Fork Santiam River Covered Bridge)

Built – 1945

Truss – Howe

Span – 105 Feet

Stream – South Santiam River

When first built it was known more commonly as the Whiskey Butte Bridge, but was renamed for a long time resident, Gordon Short.

One of the few remaining covered bridges in the county having a wooden shingle roof.

Weddle Covered Bridge
(Ames Creek Covered Bridge)

Built – 1937 *1990

Truss – Howe

Length – 120 Feet

Stream – Ames Creek

The name "Weddle" came from a nearby ranch. It is twin to the Gilkey Bridge, located about two miles away.

It had spanned Thomas Creek for 50 years, bypassed like so many others it deteriorated and became a safety issue.

Under the Oregon Covered Bridge Program it became the first to receive grants.

1989, Sweet Home Group, Known as the Cascade Forest Resource Center was formed to rebuild it in Sankey Park.

A Bridge with a House

Provides A Place for:

Weddings

Political Rallies

National Guard Drills

Religious Meetings

Town Meetings

Election Headquarters

Bond Rallies

Rainy-Day Luncheons

Kissing, secluded

Tramps a place to sleep at night

A Covered Bridge

Marion
County

Gallon House Covered Bridge
(Abiqua Creek Covered Bridge)

Built – 1917

Truss – Howe

Span – 84 Feet

Stream – Abiqua Creek

The last of Marion County's original covered bridges.

The name Gallon House is from the use of the bridge as a "pigeon drop", for liquor at the north entrance.

Operators at a liquor dispensary nearby sold "White Lightening" whiskey by the gallon to Silverton residents. Silverton was "Dry" and Mt. Angel was "Wet".

Historian Ben Maxwell in 1960 wrote about a prior bridge repair, "It still looks like an over grown doghouse-at least they could have painted it red for the sake of the conformity".

Stayton-Jordan Covered Bridge
(Salem power Canal Covered Bridge)

Built – 1998

Truss – Howe

Span – 90 Feet

Stream – Salem Power Canal

In 1986 Linn Country decided to replace the again Jordan Covered Bridge, Stayton residents asked if they could take title to it.

With the help of Marine Corps reservists for the 6th Engineering Battalion in Salem the bridge was rebuilt over the Salem Power Canal to serve as a foot bridge connecting two parks. Taking two years, a dedication ceremony was held in June 1988.

December 20, 1994 Christmas Lights on the bridge caught fire, leaving a charred remain of the covered bridge.

September 1998 a new Covered Bridge was completed, incorporated with glue laminated members for added strength.

A Bridge with a House

Became ingrained within the minds of people that almost every bridge built was covered.

1870's the idea was generally accepted, though sometimes a county court tried to save the added cost. Irate taxpayers frequently had to file petitions to have the bridge roofed, to protect their investment.

A Covered Bridge

Polk County

Ritner Covered Bridge

Built – 1927

Truss – Howe

Span – 75 Feet

Stream – Ritner Creek

Constructed by Hamer and Curry Contractors for $6,964.

It was the last covered bridge on an Oregon State Highway.

1976 the bridge was lifted from its foundation and relocated just downstream and was replaced by a concrete bridge.

Fourtner Covered Bridge

Built – 1932

Truss – Queenpost

Span – 66 Feet

Stream – South Yamhill River

Private Covered Bridge

Built by Doc Fourtner and his wife, to allow dairy livestock to cross the river.

Many of the railroad bridges were not covered; but, when a bridge collapsed under the weight of a passenger train causing it to fall into the river, the Railroad Commission's report pointed out that this bridge would have lasted longer if it had been covered.

"Not All Bridges
That Are
Covered
Are
Covered Bridges"

Cannon Covered (Street) Bridge

Built – 1988

Truss – Howe

Span – 0

Stream – None

Nothing more than an attraction in Lowell Greenway Park.

CANNON ST. BRIDGE
BUILT 1988
BY COMMUNITY SPIRIT
R. EVERLY - Hon. Bridge Supt.

Dahlenburg Covered Bridge

Built – 1989

Stream – Ames Creek

The bridge was designed and built by the construction class of Sweet Home High School.

Named after the instructor of the class,

Ben Dahlenburg.

It is a small footbridge, a scale model of the Weddle Covered Bridge.

Located in Sankey Park, Sweet Home.

Listed on the National Registry of Covered Bridges.

Whittemore Covered Bridge

Built – 1990

Stream – Stone Brook Creek

Built by Ben Dahlenburg and his students.

It once was mounted on wheels and used in local parades as a fundraiser to rebuild Weddle Covered Bridge.

Joel Whittemore was visiting Sweet Home from Virginia and bought the bridge, it was being raffled off.

He donated the bridge to the City of Sweet Home, hence the name, it permanently located at Clover Memorial Park.

Canyon Creek Covered Bridge

Built – 1976

Truss – Steel Beams

Span – 75 Feet

Stream – Canyon Creek

Not a covered bridge in the terms we define.

It is a functional pathway over Canyon Creek in Pioneer Park.

The bridge is wide enough for two people to walk through side by side.

Milo Academy Covered Bridge

(South Umpqua River Covered Bridge)

Built – 1962

Truss – Steel Girder

Span – 100 Feet

Stream – South Umpqua River

Oregon's only steel bridge housed in wood.

One of only two covered bridges in Oregon which do not have a timber truss support.

The World Guide Number (37-10-A) now ends with a letter, indicating the span is not a true truss supported bridge.

This bridge is privately owned and maintained by the Seventh Day Adventist Church.

Rock O' The Range Covered Bridge
(Swalley Canal Covered Bridge)

Built – 1963

Truss – Deck Girder

Span – 42 Feet

Stream – Swalley Canal

The World Guide Number (37-09-A) denoting that this is not a "true" covered bridge.

It is the only covered bridge span located east of the Cascade Range.

William Bowen needed to build an access across Swally Canal to his property. It was inspired by Goodpasture Covered Bridge.

Cedar Crossing Cover Bridge

(Johnson Creek Covered Bridge)

Built – 1982

Truss – Deck Girder

Span – 60 Feet

Stream – Johnson Creek

Not a covered bridge at all, it has no truss for support.

It represents Oregon's commitment to a history rich in covered bridge lore.

Cost - $93,450

$74,800 additional for related road and abutment work.

Dedicated January 1982

Interior is finished with knotty pine.

5-foot walkway separates the pedestrian and bicycle traffic from the 24-foot roadway.

A Bridge with a House

Why Bridges are Painted Red?

Make the bridge seem more like a barn to a horse, and as horses tended to be skittish above flowing water. The illusion helped farmers and travelers navigate the obstacle with little incident from their four legged friends

A Covered Bridge

References

Book
"Roofs over Rivers"
Bill & Nick Cockrell

Websights
www.oregon.com
www.oregon.gov
www.covered-bridges.org
www.coveredbridges.stateoforegon.com
www.neworegontrail.com
www.fredbecker.org
www.tfhrc.gov/structur/pubs.

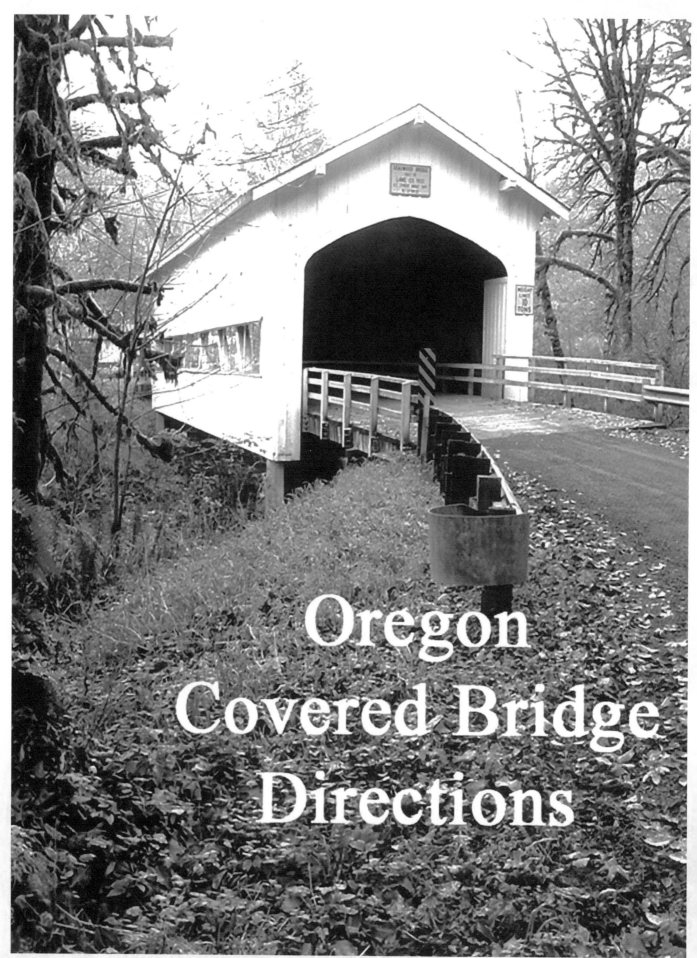

Oregon
Covered Bridge
Directions

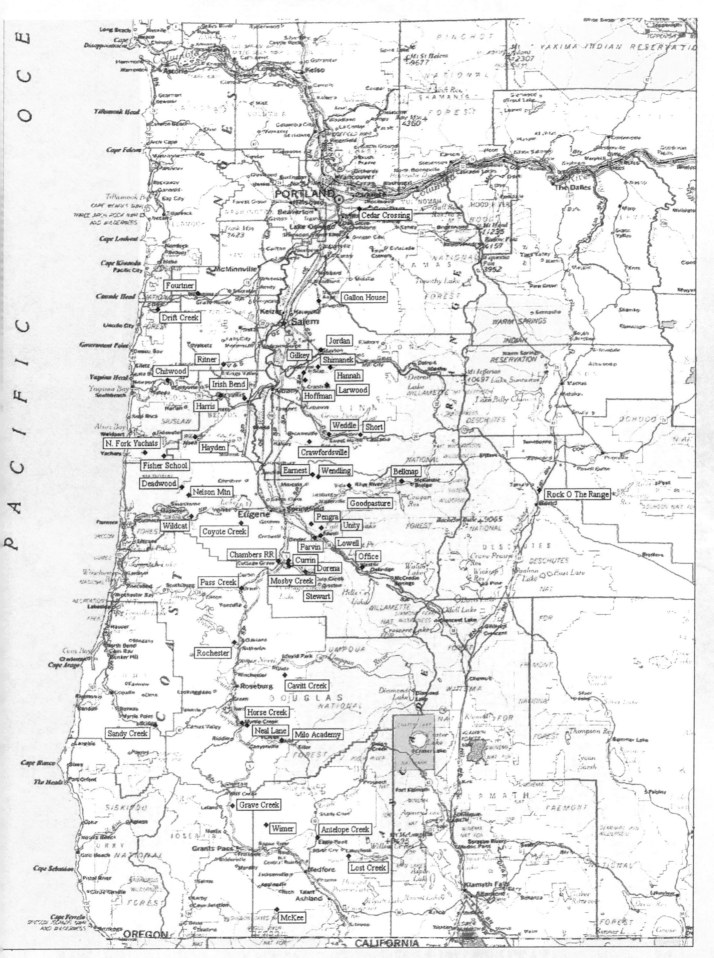

Oregon Covered Bridge Locations

County	Name	Directions	Latitude	Longitude
Benton	Harris	From Corvallis take Highway 20 through Philomath to Wren. Exit the highway, turn right twice to head back under the highway (veering) to the right at the "Y". Continue to travel west on Harris Road for approximately 2.5 miles.	44°34'48.2"N	123°27'37.1"W
Benton	Hayden	From Corvallis take Highway 34 southwest approximately 24 miles to Alsea and continue west 2 miles to Hayden Road. Turn left on Hayden Road and continue for several hundred yards to the bridge.	44°22'59.3"N	123°37'50.4"W
Benton	Irish Bend	Located on the Oregon State University campus in Corvallis. From I-5, exit 234 at Albany, travel southwest on Highway 20 to Corvallis. Follow Highway 34 southwest toward Philomath. Turn right (north) on 53rd Street and park in the County Fairgrounds on the west side of 53rd. Follow the foot path (Campus Way) on the east side of 53rd to the bridge.	44°33'59.6"N	123°18'03.3"W
Coos	Sandy Creek (Remote)	From Roseburg travel west on Highway 42 approximately 31 miles to Remote. Sandy Creek Bridge is on the north side of Highway 42, 1/4 mile west of the Remote exit.	43°00'22.8"N	123°53'30.3"W
Deschutes	Rock O' The Range	Travel two miles north of Bend on Highway 97 toward Redmond. The bridge is located on Bowery Lane, west of Highway 97.	44°07'20.6"N	121°17'12.6"W
Douglas	Cavitt Creek	From Roseburg take Highway 138 east to Glide. Just before entering Glide turn south on Little River Road. The bridge is approximately seven miles south of Highway 138 at the intersection of Little River Road and Cavitt Creek Road (county roads 17 and 82).	43°14'38.8"N	123°01'19.2"W
Douglas	Horse Creek	Exit Interstate 5 at Myrtle Creek. Follow Highway 99, the main street through downtown. The bridge is to the west in Mill Site Park.	43°01'23.7"N	123°17'23.2"W
Douglas	Milo Academy	From Canyonville travel east on Third Street and continue through Days Creek to the community of Milo. The bridge is located east of Milo at Milepost 20.5	42°56'06.8"N	123°02'20.1"W
Douglas	Neal Lane	From the city center of Myrtle Creek travel south on Main Street to Riverside Drive. Head east on Riverside Drive to Day's Creek Cut Off Road. Travel South on Day's Creek Cut-off Road to Neal Lane.	43°01'00.6"N	123°16'28.4"W
Douglas	Pass Creek	From Highway 99 (West B Street) in Drain, turn south onto 2nd Street and go one block to West A Street. Located in the city of Drain, behind Drain Civic Center at 205 W. A Street.	43°39'38.8"N	123°18'59.5"W

County	Name	Directions	Latitude	Longitude
Douglas	Rochester	From Sutherlin travel west on Highway 138 approximately two miles to Sterns Lane. Turn north on Sterns Lane to Rochester Road. The bridge is just north of the intersection of Sterns Lane and Rochester Road.	43°24'06.2"N	123°21'46.3"W
Jackson	Antelope Creek	From Highway 62 in Eagle Point, turn east onto Linn Road (sign points to Eagle Point and Klamath Falls). Travel to South Buchanan Street and turn left. Turn right onto West Main Street and continue to Royal Avenue. The bridge is located in the city of Eagle Point at the intersection of Main Street and Royal Avenue.	42°28'19.1"N	122°48'00.8"W
Jackson	Lost Creek	From Eagle Point, continue southeast on Royal Avenue to Highway 140. Alternately, travel east on Highway 140 from Highway 62, Crater Lake Highway. Continue on Highway 140 to Lake Creek Loop Road. From Lake Creek Loop Road, travel south through Lake Creek on South Fork Little Butte Creek Road. Turn south on Lost Creek Road and continue approximately one half mile. Lost Creek Bridge is 4 miles south of Lake Creek.	42°22'48.5"N	122°34'46.2"W
Jackson	McKee	From Medford travel west on Highway 238 through Jacksonville to Ruch. From Ruch head south on Applegate Road for approximately 8.5 miles.	42°07'33.0"N	123°04'21.2"W
Jackson	Wimer	From the City of Rogue River travel north on East Evans Creek Road. Turn northeast on Covered Bridge Road approximately 0.5 miles.	42°32'17.3"N	123°08'59.3"W
Josephine	Grave Creek	From Grants Pass, travel 15 miles north in Interstate 5 to Sunny Valley exit. Turn left at Sunny Valley Loop Road and continue north for about one mile. Grave Creek can be seen from I-5 and is approximately 0.25 miles from the highway.	42°38'09.0"N	123°22'39.0"W
Lane	Belknap	From Springfield take Highway 126 east approximately 46 miles to the community of McKenzie Bridge. One mile west of the small town of Rainbow, turn south on McKenzie River Drive. Follow McKenzie River Drive for about 0.8 miles to King Road West.	44°10'04.8"N	122°13'41.8"W
Lane	Chambers Railroad	Exit I-5 at Cottage Grove. Travel south on Highway 99 to Harrison Avenue. Turn west on Harrison to Old River Road. Turn south on Old River Road. Chambers RR is off of Old River Road just south of Harrison.	43°47'22.2"N	123°04'11.5"W
Lane	Coyote Creek	From Eugene travel six miles west on Highway 126 to Crow Road. Take Crow Road southwest to its intersection with Territorial Highway. Turn left (south) on Territorial Highway for one mile to Battle Creek Road. Turn right (west) on Battle Creek Road for approximately 100 yards.	43°58'11.3"N	123°19'07.8"W

County	Name	Directions	Latitude	Longitude
Lane	Currin	Travel four miles southeast of Cottage Grove on Row River Road to the intersection of Layng Road. The bridge crosses the Row River at this location and is located one mile from the Mosby Creek Bridge, also on Layng Road.	43°47'34.9"N	122°59'47.5"W
Lane	Deadwood	From Eugene, travel west to Mapleton on Highway 126. Continue northeast on Highway 36 through Swisshome 12 miles to Deadwood (or southwest from Junction City). Turn north on Lower Deadwood Road. Follow Lower Deadwood Road approximately 5 miles and turn right on Deadwood Loop Road. Deadwood Creek is on Deadwood Loop Road at Mile Point 0.3	44°08'36.9"N	123°43'13.9"W
Lane	Dorena	Travel five miles east of Cottage Grove on Row River Road to the junction of Government Road. Continue east on Government Road seven miles to the bridge.	43°44'14.6"N	122°53'01.4"W
Lane	Earnest	From I-5 exit I-105 east to Marcola Road. Follow Marcola Road approximately 14 miles. Earnest Bridge is located on Paschelke Road.	44°12'04.6"N	122°50'10.5"W
Lane	Goodpasture	From Springfield travel east on the McKenzie River Highway (Oregon Highway 126) for about 25.5 miles. Goodpasture Bridge is on Goodpasture County Road at Highway 126 just east of Vida.	44°08'53.3"N	122°35'15.9"W
Lane	Lowell	From Interstate 5 take Highway 58 east to Lowell. Alternately, from Unity follow Jasper-Lowell Road about 3 miles to Highway 58. Lowell is on the south side of Dexter Lake.	43°54'32.7"N	122°46'45.9"W
Lane	Mosby Creek	Travel one mile east of Cottage Grove on Row River Road. Follow the sign to Mosby Creek Road by turning right, and crossing the railroad track. Turn left on Mosby Creek Road and travel southeast two miles to the bridge. Alternately, from Currin Bridge continue southwest on Layng Road to Mile Point 0.2 to Mosby Creek Bridge.	43°46'41.7"N	123°00'17.2"W
Lane	Nelson Mountain	From Eugene take Highway 99 north to Highway 36. Travel west on Highway 36 approximately 38 miles to Nelson Mountain Road. Alternately, travel north from Mapleton on Highway 36. The Nelson Mountain Road turnoff is located near milepost 17. Turn south on Nelson Mountain Road to the bridge.	44°06'15.6"N	123°40'25.1"W
Lane	Office	From Interstate 5 take Highway 58 east towards Oakridge. Just before entering Oakridge, near milepost 31, turn west onto Westridge Ave. Continue to Westfir on County Road 6128. Travel about 2.5 miles to the mill site, community and bridge.	43°45'30.3"N	122°29'44.5"W

County	Name	Directions	Latitude	Longitude
Lane	Parvin	From I-5 take Highway 58 east to Dexter, just west of Lowell. Turn south on Lost Creek Road. Turn right onto Rattlesnake Road from Lost Creek Road at Mile Point 1.8, and follow Rattlesnake west for 0.5 miles. Turn south on Lost Valley Lane to Parvin Road. Alternately, exit Highway 58 at Lost Creek Road and travel southeast to Parvin Road. Continue south on Parvin Road to the bridge.	43°53'58.0"N	122°49'22.8"W
Lane	Pengra	From I-5 take Highway 58 east to Parkway Road. Follow Parkway Road north to the community of Jasper. Turn southeast on Jasper-Lowell Road for about 3 miles. Turn left (east) on Little Falls Creek Road and travel 1/4 mile to Place Road.	43°57'57.7"N	122°50'43.5"W
Lane	Stewart	Travel one mile east of Cottage Grove on Row River Road. Follow the sign to Mosby Creek Road, turning right and crossing the railroad tracks. Turn left (south) on Mosby Creek Road and travel approximately 3.5 miles to Garoutte Road.	43°45'57.5"N	122°59'38.9"W
Lane	Unity	From Interstate 5 exit Highway 58 and travel east to the town of Lowell. Turn left at the Lowell Covered Bridge and continue north through Lowell on County Road 6220 (Lowell-Unity Road) for two miles to Unity.	43°56'41.2"N	122°46'30.5"W
Lane	Wendling	From Springfield, follow 14th Street in Springfield and travel northeast (as it becomes Marcola Road) to Marcola. At Marcola, turn right (east onto Wendling Road and follow the road to the bridge. Alternately, from Earnest Bridge, follow Paschelke Road about 1.3 miles to Wendling Road. Turn east on Wendling Road to Mile Point 3.5.	44°11'28.0"N	122°47'55.7"W
Lane	Wildcat	Travel 33 miles west of Eugene on Oregon Highway 126 to Whitaker Creek /Clay Creek Recreation Area turnoff. Exit the highway on the south side and follow the road back under the highway and railroad tracks (north) a short distance to the bridge.	44°00'10.8"N	123°39'17.3"W
Lincoln	Chitwood	From Interstate 5, take the Corvallis exit (228) west 38 miles through Philomath on US 20. The bridge adjoins Highway 20 near milepost 17. Alternately, travel east from Newport on Highway 20, 17 miles to Chitwood.	44°39'15.2"N	123°49'03.9"W

County	Name	Directions	Latitude	Longitude
Lincoln	Drift Creek	From Lincoln City head north on Hwy. 101 to Hwy. 18. Travel east on Hwy. 18 to milepost 3.96. Exit Hwy. 18 and travel south on Bear Creek Road 0.9 mile. The bridge is located on the left.	44°59'35.1"N	123°53'11.2"W
Lincoln	Fisher School	From Interstate 5, take the Corvallis exit (228) west 38 miles through Philomath on US 20. Follow Highway 34 southwest through Alsea and continue 20 miles west to the Five Rivers-Fisher Road (Forest Service Road 141). Turn south at the fork at Siletz Road. Continue left past Buck Creek Road about one mile to the bridge. Alternately from Yachats, travel east on Forest Service Road 1560 about 20 miles. This route is not recommended because the road is extremely rough and steep. Note: Forest Service Road 141 connects to the Deadwood Bridge in Lane County.	44°17'29.8"N	123°50'28.3"W
Lincoln	North Fork Yachats	From Yachats travel approximately 7 miles east on Yachats River Road to N Yachats River Road. At the intersection turn north and travel approximately 1.5 miles.	44°18'35.9"N	123°58'10.9"W
Linn	Crawfordsville	From Interstate 5 take Highway 228 (exit 216) east through Brownsville to Crawfordsville. Crawfordsville Bridge is located at the west end of Crawfordsville, beside Highway 228.	44°21'26.8"N	122°51'38.2"W
Linn	Gilkey	From Interstate 5 exit 238 and travel east to Jefferson. Just east of the arch bridge over the Santiam River, turn right on South Main Street and continue until the street turns into Jefferson-Scio Drive. Continue east towards Scio and turn right (south) onto Robinson Drive. As Robinson Drive curves east, turn right on Goar Road and travel 1.5 miles to the bridge. Alternately, travel one-half mile south of Scio on Highway 226, then three miles west on Gilkey Road. Turn north on Goar Road and travel 0.5 mile to the bridge.	44°41'16.4"N	122°54'11.9"W
Linn	Hannah	From Interstate 5, exit 238 and travel east to Jefferson. Just east of the arch bridge over the Santiam River, turn right on South Main Street and continue until the street becomes Jefferson-Scio Drive. Continue east into Scio and turn left onto Highway 226. Follow Highway 226 approximately six miles west to Camp Morrison Drive and turn right (south). Alternately, exit Highway 226 from Interstate 5 in Albany and travel to Scio.	44°42'43.3"N	122°43'07.3"W

County	Name	Directions	Latitude	Longitude
Linn	Hoffman	From I-5 at Albany take Highway 226 (US Route 20) (exit 233) east to Crabtree Drive. Exit the highway and travel to the town of Crabtree. From Crabtree travel north on Hungry Hill Drive for approximately 1 mile.	44°39'11.8"N	122°53'25.2"W
Linn	Larwood	From I-5 at Albany take Highway 226 (US Route 20) (exit 233) east to Crabtree. From Crabtree travel east on Highway 226 approximately 1 mile to Fish Hatchery Drive. Travel east on Fish Hatchery Road for approximately 6 miles.	44°37'49.1"N	122°44'26.8"W
Linn	Shimanek	From Interstate 5 exit 238 and travel east to Jefferson. Just east of the arch bridge over the Santiam River, turn right on South Main Street and continue until the street becomes Jefferson-Scio Drive. Continue east into Scio and turn left onto Highway 226. Follow Highway 226 two miles east and turn left (north) onto Richardson Gap Road.	44°42'56.2"N	122°48'15.5"W
Linn	Short	From Interstate 5 at Albany exit US Route 20 (exit 233) southeast through Lebanon and Sweet Home for 37 miles to Cascadia. West of the city limits of Cascadia, turn left at High Deck Road. Alternately, exit Interstate 5 at exit 216 and travel east through Crawfordsville to Sweet Home. Turn right on Highway 20 and continue to High Deck Road.	44°23'29.6"N	122°30'35.5"W
Linn	Weddle	From Interstate 5 at Albany exit US Route 20 (exit 233) southeast through Lebanon to Sweet Home. From Highway 20 turn south at 12th Avenue. Turn east on Kalmia Street and then south on 14th Avenue for two blocks. Sankey Park is on the left. Alternately, exit Interstate 5 at exit 216 and travel east through Crawfordsville to Sweet Home	44°23'35"N	122°43'39"W
Marion	Gallon House	From Salem travel north on Highway 213 (Silverton Road NE) about 14 miles to Silverton. At Silverton travel north on Highway 214 to Hobart Road. Turn west on Hobart to Gallon House Road (0.5 mi.). Turn north on Gallon House Road.	45°01'55.5"N	122°47'53.3"W
Marion	Stayton-Jordan	From Interstate 5 take Salem Exit 253 east on Highway 22 for 15 miles to the Stayton /Sublimity turnoff. Travel south one mile to Stayton. Turn east on Marion Street to Pioneer Park.	44°47'55.2"N	122°47'09.2"W
Multnomah	Cedar Crossing	From I-205 exit Foster Road east. Turn south on SE 134 to Deardorf Road and travel for 1/2 mile. Cedar Crossing is on Deardorf Road over Johnson Creek.	45°28'19.3"N	122°31'25.4"W

County	Name	Directions	Latitude	Longitude
Polk	Fourtner	From Portland take Highway 99 through Newberg to Highway 18, then west 60 miles past Willamina to New Grand Ronde. Turn north on Grand Ronde Road to "A" Ackerson Road. Turn left and continue one block, keeping left at the "Y" into the yard of the white house. Be sure to request permission at the house before proceeding past the barn to the bridge.	45°04'14.1"N	123°36'59.1"W
Polk	Ritner Creek	From Interstate 5 exit 258 and follow Portland Road 5 miles to the junction of Highway 22 (Marion Street). Turn right (west) crossing the Willamette River, and continue 17 miles to Dallas. From Dallas travel south on Highway 223 approximately 12 miles through Pedee. Ritner Creek Bridge is approximately 3.5 miles south of Pedee.	44°43'41.1"N	123°26'30.9"W